COLOR YOUR
MANDALA

COLOR YOUR
MANDALA

Discover your Creativity by Coloring

Ancient Symbols

Cassandra Lorius

CICO BOOKS

LONDON NEW YORK

This book is dedicated to Paul Standheven, energy healer, who supported me at a dark moment in my life. We initially worked on developing these meditations jointly, until the mandalas gave me a focus and frame for my life and held me in their magical circles.

This edition published in 2010 exclusively for Direct Brands by CICO Books
an imprint of Ryland Peters & Small
20–21 Jockey's Fields, London WC1R 4BW
www.cicobooks.com

10 9 8 7 6 5 4 3 2 1

Text © Cassandra Lorius 2010
Design and illustrations © CICO Books 2010

A CIP catalog record for this book is available from the British Library and Library of Congress.

ISBN-13: 978-1-907030-49-9

Printed in China

Editor: Alison Wormleighton
Design concept: David Fordham, Jerry Goldie
Illustrations: Stephen Dew pp 21, 27 (color wheels), 32 (below), 33, 34 (below), 35, 36 (below), 37, 38 (below), 39, 40 (below), 41, 42–45, 58–59, 98–99, 102–103; all other illustrations by Melissa Launay.

CONTENTS

"Dance" (page 71) depicts Lord Shiva, who
dances the world into creation.

INTRODUCTION: MANDALAS, CIRCLES OF WHOLENESS

A mandala is a pattern of power that represents the whole circle of existence. Its circular shape encloses a depiction of a holistic cosmos. Mandala shapes naturally occur in the organic world; their perfect forms can be seen in atomic structures, crystals, and flowers, as well as solar systems and wave forms. I like the description by the Mandala Project (an online gallery) of a mandala as a primal circular pattern that has existed in nature since the beginning of time.

SPIRITUAL JOURNEYS

Anthropologists have discovered that representations of mandalas have long been used in many cultures as vehicles for shamanic journeys. Navajo Indians, for example, created sand mandalas, which described journeys into the spirit realm in a similar way to the Aboriginal bark or rock paintings of dreamtime. Among the Navajo, sand paintings were completed by the medicine man, who used them in healing rituals. I have seen fabulous photographs of a shamanic ritual conducted with a young boy sitting inside a section of the sand map, used as a therapeutic rite designed to banish disease.

Mandalas can be colored and meditated upon as a path to power, describing an inner journey to the center. The center is both a point of focus and the source of creation—represented in Indian mandalas as a primal dot (bindi) in the center. Many cultures have a tradition of using painted or made images in mandala designs during rituals to facilitate altered states of consciousness. These are used as circles of empowerment. Therefore, a wider definition of mandalas is that they exist as holistic diagrams encompassing a spiritual approach to our self-development, healing, and growth.

This kit will enable you to explore mandalas for your own personal process.

Above and right: "Looking" (page 66) depicts the third eye. "Connecting with the Cosmos" (page 72) invites us to identify with a holistic perspective.

TANTRA AND TANTRIC BUDDHISM

Traditional mandalas are particularly associated with tantric Hinduism and Buddhism. For millennia, Hindu tantrics used geometric designs called yantras to symbolize a spiritual understanding of reality. The author Ajit Mookerjee describes them as "thought forms." They are not merely representations of the transcendent realm but depict potential energies that can be processed during meditation practice. Within tantra there are also invocation practices, or mantra, which involve repeating sacred words or sounds to harmonize humans with the divine.

In mystical traditions, sacred texts are read as metaphors, alluding to inner states of mind as opposed to the outer experience of reality. Now that we have digested some of this precious material in our own culture, we can spell out the psychological dimensions of spiritual texts and apply them in a variety of valuable ways.

WHAT IS TANTRA?

The Sanskrit word "tantra" has a multiplicity of meanings, referring to texts and practices that weave threads of connection between texts and lived experience. They also refer to rituals that enliven our energy body and incorporate it into meditation and other spiritual practices. Tantra utilizes our sensory experience of living in a body to facilitate transformation, rather than denying the body and its desires as so many other traditions do. In fact, a tantric perspective is that literally embodying change and living through emotional and psychic transformation of human experience provides a fast track to enlightenment.

Left: A mandala made from flower petals to celebrate the Onam festival, which takes place every fall in Kerala, India.

Left, below: Detail from the Shri yantra (Divine Love, page 54).

Right: A fifteenth-century Nepalese mandala of Hevajra painted on cotton depicts a god and goddess in union surrounded by a pantheon of Buddhist demons and deities.

Tantra comprises a collection of pre-Hindu traditions that are now also woven into the Vajrayana school of Tibetan Buddhism. The very different attitude to the relationship between divine and human is most clearly seen in the practice of deity visualizations. In deity practices you focus on a god or goddess whose qualities you aspire to, and imagine that their body merges with your own, in order to incorporate their divine qualities. Creating and coloring your own deity mandala and meditating upon it is a unique way to power your personal development; see the Deity Practice mandala on pages 80–81.

MYSTICAL MANDALAS

All mandalas depict spiritual planes of reality. Tibetan Buddhists, for example, work with mandalas to map the sacred abodes of the gods, Buddhas, bodhisattvas (the aspiring Buddhas), and dakinis (sky-dancers), within whom infinite wisdom and compassion are manifested.

Some mandalas illustrate the obstacles that have to be overcome in order to cultivate compassion and wisdom; these obstacles may be depicted in the form of terrifying demons, which manifest in our lives as negative emotions. Meditating upon your psychological journey, and allowing your own demons to take form as you color your mandala, gives you food for thought about your own personal limitations and resistance to change.

Another lovely ritual use of mandalas is the Tibetan practice of designing and creating elaborate sand mandalas (see below), such as the Kalachakra. Part of the purpose of this esoteric ritual is to demonstrate the impermanence of our present lives and physical condition. When monks wash away the beautiful and highly intricate mandalas that have taken many days to create, they believe that this dissolves the energy created through spiritual practice and releases its merit. By mixing the sand into streams, rivers, and oceans, this merit spreads through them and benefits the world. In 1973 the spiritual head of Tibetan Buddhism, the Dalai Lama, first permitted monks to make the Kalachakra "Wheel of Time" sand mandala in public. This intricate mandala has long been used for tantric initiation.

Left: Buddhist monks used sand to create this mandala. After completion, the sand will be placed in a stream to spread the mandala's spiritual blessing.

Right: A sixteenth-century Tibetan mandala depicting Buddha Vairocana. The geometric devices of a cross, a square in a circle, the four corners, and an inner ring of lotus petals show how existence can embrace polarities.

OUTSIDE THE EASTERN TRADITION

Mandala patterns may also be found in non-Eastern mystic traditions. They can be seen in the rose windows of cathedrals such as Chartres and Notre Dame in France, both dating from the thirteenth century, which inspire us with their beauty and transcendent power as they filter heavenly light. A rose window inspired the design of the Grace mandala shown on page 123.

Through the centuries, mandalas have informed the work of mystics, such as the twelfth-century nun Hildegard of Bingen. In her illustrated book *Scivias* she published visionary mandalas depicting circles of angelic beings in celebration of God's creation. Similar rituals are found in ancient traditions. For instance, the labyrinth, a maze-like pathway that could be literally walked in order to gain power and insight, is found in many cultures around the world.

Right: The north rose window at Chartres cathedral, France, dating from 1223.

Below: An image taken from *Scivias,* by Hildegard of Bingen, illustrating her vision of a choir of angels.

The classical labyrinth is thought to date back several thousand years, while a more complex version became popular during the Middle Ages; labyrinths still exist in the floors of many European churches. The most famous, dating back to about 1200, is at Chartres, where the walking of the labyrinth won as much spiritual merit as going on the established, church-sanctioned pilgrimage to Jerusalem. Walking the labyrinth is just one expression of a basic human need for connection and wholeness.

The Hajj, the Islamic pilgrimage to Mecca, involves seven circumambulations of a central building, the Ka'ba, the holiest place in Islam. This square in the middle of a circle can be seen in mystical terms as reconciling a geometrical shape with the universal and holistic shape of the circle.

Among the Sufi orders, the Mevlevi dervishes, or whirling dervishes, use the ritual of a whirling dance as a means of prayer. Their spinning circles symbolize the elliptical orbits of planets around the sun.

JUNG AND MANDALA PAINTING

Within traditional cultures, from Navajo to Tibetan, mandalas are used to help attune man's awareness to his place in a holistic world, and these indigenous traditions have been mined for decades by Western spiritual practitioners. The pioneer of this approach was the Swiss psychological explorer Carl Jung (1875–1961), who encouraged his clients to regularly paint their own mandalas. Over the course of psychotherapy, Jung noticed that his clients generated mandalas with meaningful symbols from their own unconscious—even where they had had no previous contact with traditional mandalas. Because these forms have arisen in many disparate cultures over millennia, emerging spontaneously in dreams and drawings, Jung came to the conclusion that mandalas expressed universal archetypes. He considered each individual's artwork to be a personal manifestation of a collective unconscious common to all humanity.

Above: The Grace mandala (page 123) is an example of sacred art based upon geometry. This mandala was inspired by the intricate stained-glass designs of cathedral rose windows.

THE SELF AND INDIVIDUATION

Jung saw mandalas as an archetypal expression of our own personal journey to self-development. According to psychoanalysts, personal growth is the most compelling goal in life, once basic survival needs have been satisfied. Jung found mandalas an extremely potent means of self-development, and he used this method effectively with his clients, demonstrating how each person's mandalas evolved over years of work.

Jung saw the ideal world contained within a mandala as representing an integrated world and he claimed that a mandala functions as a personal guide to becoming integrated. He saw the mandala as symbolizing the perfect wholeness of the self. In *Man and his Symbols,* Jung described the practice of making a mandala as a way to integrate scattered parts of oneself, creating a center and coalescing into a unified whole around this center.

Each of us has a story that we tell about ourself—it makes up our identity. Jung believed that if our personal reality has been denied by our family and schooling or has been rejected by others (or ourself), we risk psychological disintegration. Although he believed that a human being is fundamentally self-knowing, he felt that most of us have lost touch with important parts of ourselves. Rediscovering our own

Above and left: The journey of the self. The human figure has a rainbow body, which projects into the environment. The Childhood mandala (page 103) is used for integrating aspects of the past.

14

story can facilitate integration and healing. By exploring the messages of our dreams and imagination, we can rediscover and reintegrate our different facets. The goal of life, according to Jung, is self-realization, which he called individuation—the process of getting to know, expressing, and making constructive relationships between the various components of the self and living in accordance with these processes. We all have a specific nature that is uniquely our own, and unless this is fulfilled through a union of our conscious and our unconscious, we may become unbalanced or ill. If we can recognize and accept our uniqueness, we can use ourselves as a guide to embark on a process of individuation and tap into our true self. We do not have to be content with our limited horizons, but can embrace self-awareness in order to reach a higher state of consciousness.

Jung believed that this journey of transformation is at the mystical heart of all religions.

THE STARTING POINT

Jung's approach is the starting point for this book. The artwork and imagery that individuals generate from their unconscious are particularly valid for that person, and the mandala forms that contemporary artists generate are also very relevant and inspiring.

Melissa Launay, the principal artist, and I have developed highly personal interpretations of the theme of mandalas, freely drawing on the iconography and associations of more traditional mandalas while finding our own expression. Many contemporary artists are likewise using mandala patterns and principles to create inspirational art, incorporating elements of balance and harmony to create an evocative whole.

These mandalas are offered as the starting point for your own journey of self-realization. Creating mandalas provides an opportunity for everyone to nurture this quality in themselves, and I trust that some of the themes I have chosen to develop are relevant to your needs right now.

Above and right: Details from mandalas on depression (above) and death (right and page 135) explore the shadow side of the human psyche.

15

The Compassion mandala (page 56) shows the Buddhist
goddess Tara holding a lotus, symbol of transformation.

HOW TO WORK WITH THIS KIT

Color Your Mandala is designed to spark your creative fire by coloring and creating mandalas, either following the given designs or by composing or coloring your own mandala using a combination of the following tools:

Stencils The six stencils in this kit relate to the following mandalas: Awareness (page 52); Divine Love (Shri Yantra, page 54); Relationship (page 94); Earth (page 108); Looking (page 66), and Grace (page 123). The stencils give the primary lines for each design, along with its key symbols.

Stencil symbols Use the stencil symbols to recreate the mandala, or combine them to make a new piece of art. The mandalas on pages 42–45 have been composed in this way—the artist took a selection of stencil symbols, such as the lotus from Divine Love and the leaf from the Earth mandala, to create new patterns and textures.

Mandala outlines Thirty sheets of paper printed with mandala outlines are included for those of you who want to focus just on the detail, filling in your own pattern or using the stencil symbols.

Coloring book The coloring book includes complete line art for 30 mandala designs, so you can focus on experimenting with color rather than form.

This guide book explores the significance of color in mandalas, and lists a range of mandala symbols and what they mean so you can select them according to the effect or energy you want your mandala to generate. Each mandala painting also comes with colorway suggestions to help you visualize various color combinations.

COLOR AS A CREATIVE PATHWAY

When we color, we create and recreate ancient motifs that express beliefs, from the healing bowl held by a medicine Buddha to the yin - yang symbol. Even what we would consider purely decorative has meaning—simple patterns of flowers or repeating hearts affirms the beauty of an idea. Coloring connects us with nature, with ourselves, helping us give life to something in a uniquely personal way.

Color is an intrinsic part of many spiritual and esoteric traditions. It can be used in meditation and therapy: coloring a motif helps focus the mind and encourage a connection with our selves—we can be completely "in the moment." It is a beautiful means of bringing us into our own presence, which is deeply empowering. In this state we are most creative, using our senses and intuition to create freely and bypass the part of the mind that judges or intellectualizes our work, potentially blocking our flow.

TRADITIONAL MANDALA COLORS

In traditional mandala painting, colors had clear symbolic meanings:

Yellow, as the color of earth, symbolized rootedness, stoicism, and equanimity.

Aquamarine blue seen in the lapis lazuli stone, which is veined with gold, was associated with dazzling sky, evoking infinity through association with the heavens.

Gold has always been considered precious, and symbolized spiritual prosperity and divinity in traditional paintings. It was also associated with longevity and eternity.

Purple has been valued particularly since Roman times, as it was a greatly expensive dye made from crushed murex shells from Lebanon, and was thus the prerogative of the nobility and royalty. Purple

Celtic colors

For the Tree of Life Mandala, the artist used non-traditional colors that give an earthy, natural feel, reminiscent of Celtic decoration.

Olive green

Emerald green

Leaf green

Deep red

Pale yellow

is worn by Christan officiates and associated with the crown chakra (see page 23) in the Hindu mapping of the subtle body, where it represents the goal of enlightenment.

Red The red of traditional mandalas both represents and facilitates powerful rituals. It is the color of passion, transmuted through ritual actions into wisdom.

It has wide cross cultural associations with fire and blood. Red is therefore considered the color of the life force, action, and fire. Red is commonly associated with sexuality, blood, and therefore danger. Because of its association with fire we attribute red with dynamic qualities of energy and passion. For many of us, red has full-blooded, exciting, and even aggressive connotations.

INTERPRETING COLOR

Artists have long known that colors can create atmosphere and affect our emotions and mood. How these qualities are described is different depending on the cultural context.

Red, green, and blue have similar connotations across cultures, because of their associations with blood, vegetation, and the sky and sea. However, some colors like black and white can be subject to quite a different interpretation. For instance, the black many of us might regard negatively is also seen to represent transformation in some spiritual traditions. These traditions also value negative emotions, because they provide raw material to be transformed into spiritually evolved qualities, such as wisdom and compassion.

Whereas in Western society black is strongly associated with death, the Tibetan tradition of nagtang mandalas depicts red and gold deities emerging from a black background

This detail from a mandala of negative emotions evokes a tradition of positive value in emotions such as grief, anger, guilt, or jealousy, which are all grist to the mill.

which, like our modern understanding of space contains all the possibilities of creation. Therefore the Buddhist perspective on the void of infinite space is one of resting in vastness rather than fear-inducing annihilation.

As a color, black absorbs all light in the spectrum (whereas white reflects light back). Pagans see black as protective, as it can absorb negative energy. An object doesn't emit light that color, it absorbs light waves except for the frequency we see as that color —so we only see an object as red or green or black because we perceive it that way, and not because redness or greenness is part of its essential nature.

COLOR THEORY

Scientist and alchemist Isaac Newton formulated the basis of current color theory, categorizing the colors that separated out when white light was passed through a spectrum into the hierarchy of seven hues that is still commonly used today; red, orange, yellow, green, blue, indigo, and violet (see page 23). His ideas

The primary colors according to Steiner

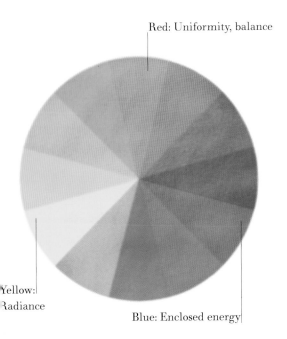

Red: Uniformity, balance

Yellow: Radiance

Blue: Enclosed energy

and yellow to produce green he considered that the spiritual aspect of cold blue would be imbued with the emotional warmth of yellow. For Kandinsky, black was "a silence with no possibilities... something burnt out, like the ashes of a funeral pyre... The silence of black is the silence of death," whereas he attributed white with a "harmony of silence... like many pauses in music," while violet was "sad, extinguished." Just as orange is red brought nearer to humanity by yellow, so violet is red withdrawn from humanity by blue. For Kandinsky, yellow was a color representation of "madness" or "maniacal rage."

Color associations according to Kandinsky

incorporated what we would today regard as mystical thinking about the correspondence of colors to the planets and the musical scale—in which the number seven was particularly important.

Philosopher and founder of the Steiner movement, Rudolf Steiner believed that colors had their own particular energy; yellow having a radiating movement, and blue an enclosing energy field.

Artists such as Wassily Kandinsky were preoccupied with the spiritual resonance of color. In his work *Concerning the Spiritual in Art* (1910), Kandinsky described colors as "vibrations of the soul" which could be arranged along a spectrum from warm to cold and light to dark. For instance, in mixing blue

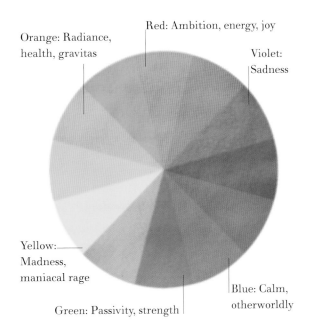

Orange: Radiance, health, gravitas

Red: Ambition, energy, joy

Violet: Sadness

Yellow: Madness, maniacal rage

Green: Passivity, strength

Blue: Calm, otherworldly

COLOR IS PERSONAL

Despite the common associations we often share about color, I think the above quotations from Kandinsky demonstrate vividly that our response to color is intensely personal.

Each of us has our own strong reactions to color, built up through cultural and personal experience. For instance, past experiences can lead us to associate specific colors with certain emotions. For Rudolf Steiner art was primarily a means of creating a bridge between the spiritual and physical world, while for Jung we have seen that it was a gateway to the unconscious. For artists, it's an expressive language for depicting your internal experience.

A COLOR-BATH MEDITATION

You can develop your unique sensitivity toward the qualities of different colors by saturating yourself in their energy—this could be standing in a green field or lying under a blue sky. It could be gazing at a screen of that color, or imagining the color.

Each individual color is a particular frequency of light wave, and a very simple meditation to experiment with your response to color is to imagine saturating your body with different colors in turn. This is what some artists do when they meditate on colors, allowing their inner awareness to guide them toward a particular palette and certain combinations of colors.

The easiest way to do this is to use the same sequence of colors described by Newton which were ascribed by the Hindus to chakras, or energy wheels in the body, starting from red at the base of your spine, and upward through orange, yellow, green, blue, indigo, and violet; see the Chakras and Color chart opposite.

CHAKRAS AND COLOR

There are at least seven chakras on the body, situated from the base of the spine to the crown. Each chakra has an associated color. The sequence of colors, beginning with red at the base of the spine, is a useful structure to follow when meditating with colors, and chimes with our knowledge of the hues in the spectrum of light.

Red is associated with energy and the **base chakra**, sited at the tailbone. It is considered the home of our unawakened vital energy.

Orange The **sacral chakra** in the womb is orange, and associated with creativity.

Yellow is the color of the **solar plexus chakra** and happiness, which like the sun is concerned with manifesting our creativity in the world.

Green The **heart chakra** is colored green and is associated with love, healing, and nurturing.

The body's principle chakra points from base to crown chakras.

Blue The **throat chakra** is colored blue and is associated with expressing ourselves in words.

Indigo The chakra at the **third eye** is indigo and associated with vision and insight—so indigo is considered to stimulate the development of our unique vision.

Violet The chakra at the **crown of the head** is violet. It encourages a sense of bliss at our connectedness with the creative energy of the universe.

WHAT ATTRACTS YOU TO A COLOR?

The color red represents vitality, creativity, energy, and power, as well as celebration; in China, red is the color of weddings. People who love red aim to be at the center of the action, where they receive maximum attention. Restless and impulsive, red encourages determination and will power. Red keeps you firmly in the present and stimulates your senses; it has a long, slow wavelength, and fires your energy powerfully.

Orange is also energizing, lifting your spirit from depression to happiness. It facilitates your creative impulses, and in color therapy is reputed to help release deeper emotions underlying your doubts or sadness. Orange encourages you to let go and live life with less inhibition.

If you are attracted to yellow, you are probably optimistic, with good communication skills. Yellow is classically associated with intellectual stimulus, and is believed to encourage self-worth.

The color green balances, creating harmony and connecting us to feelings of love and care for the natural world. It also encourages growth and ideas.

Blue is the color of truth, faith, and serenity which creates a cool and calm atmosphere. Eternity, chastity, and devotion are some of the associations that appear in many different cultures. Blue is omnipresent throughout the churches of Catholic Europe in the robes of the Virgin Mary—and early sky gods such as the ancient Egyptian goddess, Nut.

The color indigo, once a rare dye made from the indigo plant, is associated with the mysterious and the profound. If you are attracted to this color, it can mean that you like to penetrate beyond surface appearances.

Traditionally, indigo links to the higher mind, promoting a sense of vision.

In many spiritual traditions violet is known as a very powerful color, and has strong links with creativity.

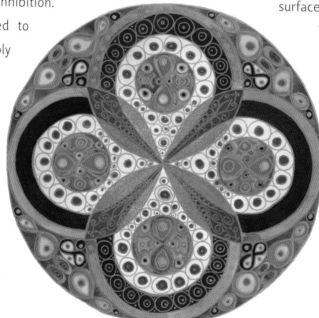

COLOR ASSOCIATIONS

RED: Energy, passion, power, spontaneity, intensity, desire

ORANGE: Creativity, pleasure

YELLOW: Optimism, confidence, personal power

GREEN: Harmony, growth, youthful vigor

BLUE: Serenity, truth, faith

DARK BLUE: Authority

PURPLE: Spirituality, royalty, mystery

PINK: Love

WHITE: Purity, immortality

BLACK: Dominance, mortality

BROWN: Grounding, earthy

GOLD: The sun, masculinity, wisdom, prosperity

SILVER: The moon, the Goddess, femininity, reflection, insight, intuition

COLOR TECHNIQUES

Every artist dips his brush in his own soul,
and paints his own nature into his pictures.
-Henry Ward Beecher (1813-1887)

Let your personal responses to colors guide you in choosing a palette for your mandala. Lay out your materials, whether pastel, paints, pencils, or papers for collage, and choose the colors that appeal to you. With an open mind, wait to see what sort of mood the color evokes in you as you work. Let the color lead on to the next color you wish to work with.

While painting mandalas, the picture may seem to develop out of itself, and sometimes in spite of what you were intending to draw. There is no right or wrong way of approaching drawing a mandala. If you wish to open yourself to inspiration, many artists who work with mandalas advise a period of quiet reflection or meditation before embarking on creating one, in order to still the mind and access deeper levels of awareness. (See the simple meditation on color on page 29, and on page 22).

CREATING VIBRANCY

During my art degree I learnt about underpainting complementary colors to create vibrancy. The color underneath can still be detected, and makes the top layer more alive and dynamic, as in Monet's use of purple and orange, or Rothko's red underpainted with green. Complementary colors sit opposite each other on the color wheel (see opposite): they are commonly considered to be red and green, orange and blue, and yellow and purple. Complementary colors appear vibrant to the eye because the visual processing of color in the brain seems to be stimulated by the opposition of complementary colors in nature, as well as by distinctions between light and dark. Tone therefore is also important.

To create the effect of luminosity using shading, you can also underpaint with white, or build up images with white and pastel color to create more depth and brilliance.

White is made up of all the colors of the spectrum, and you can work with it to make the other colors you are working with more luminous. Working it into primary colors gives an effect of radiating light. White occurs when the whole spectrum of light is seen together or when red, yellow, and blue colors are mixed; therefore everything is present within white.

You can also pick out details of your mandala with golds and silvers—medieval monks working in libraries decorated their holy books with gold leaf. In many cultures, gold has also been associated with the sun, and silver with lunar qualities. Wisdom texts are illuminated in this way.

Working with complementary colors

The traditional color wheel shows complementary colors sitting opposite one another on the wheel: yellow and violet, orange and blue, and red and green. Other theories link cyan with red; magenta with green, blue, and yellow.

Violet and yellow combine with blue and orange, using two sets of complementaries to create vibrancy of color.

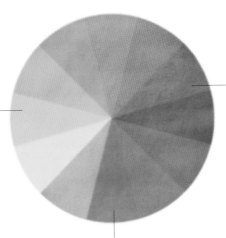

This mandala uses the complementary colors blue and orange.

Red and green interplay in this vibrant mandala image of a laughing Buddha.

When coloring in your mandala in the coloring book, work out a color scheme before you begin, trying out different color combinations.

27

The mandala above was designed with the theme of love
in mind. The artist, Melissa Launay, worked with reds,
oranges, and pinks, and intensified their effect by
contrasting with delicate blues.

A COLOR MEDITATION BEFORE YOU BEGIN

The circular shape of the mandala helps you to focus inward, into what is contained within the circle. In Jungian terms, the circle represents your self or your psyche. Using color to develop your mandala will allow you to go deeper into your own personal experience. Colors can affect your mood and bring emotions to the surface. Look at other mandalas for inspiration, or meditate on your favorite colors before starting your mandala. You can intensify the experience by working to music that may also encourage you to go deeper within.

To start with a color meditation, lie down and imagine drawing the color you prefer into your body on the in-breath. Let it saturate your body as you slowly breathe out. Breathe more of that color in on the in-breath. If you don't have an immediate color preference, start with red, breathing it into your body and saturating your being. Then move on to orange, then yellow, green, blue, indigo, and violet, stopping when you feel an affinity with a color. Focus on the color and let different moods, emotions, and sensations arise, guiding you in creating your personal mandala. Let the mandala draw itself.

How To Work with the Mandala Stencils

Six stencils are included in this kit, so you can create the following mandalas: Awareness (page 52); Divine Love (Shri Yantra, page 54); Relationship (page 94); Earth (page 108); Looking (page 66), and Grace (page 123). The stencils give the primary outlines for each design, along with its key symbols. The following pages show how each mandala progresses from stencil to the page, plus ideas showing how you might build layers of color. Pages 42–45 show four original mandalas created by artist Stephen Dew, who took all of the symbols from the stencils and combined them to create four new mandalas.

Awareness Mandala

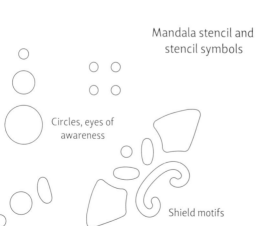

Mandala stencil and stencil symbols

Circles, eyes of awareness

Shield motifs

30

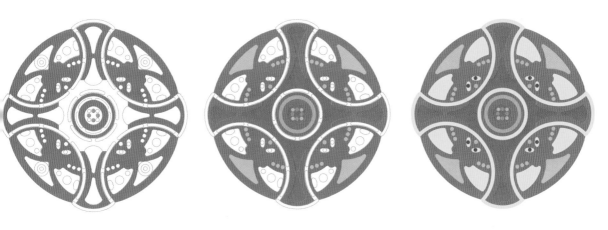

Color layers

Divine Love Mandala

Mandala stencil and
stencil symbols

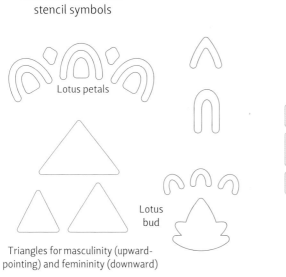

Lotus petals

Lotus
bud

Triangles for masculinity (upward-
pointing) and femininity (downward)

Color layers

Relationship Mandala

Mandala stencil and
stencil symbols

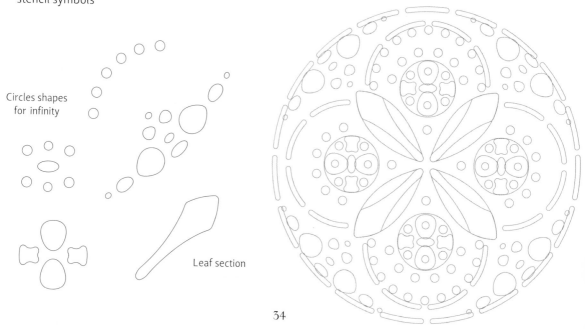

Circles shapes
for infinity

Leaf section

Color layers

Earth Mandala

Mandala stencil and
stencil symbols

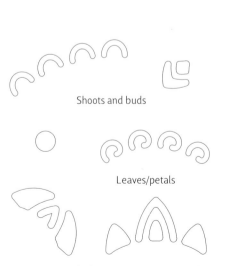

Shoots and buds

Leaves/petals

Color layers

Looking Mandala

Mandala stencil and
stencil symbols

Water/leaf

All-seeing eye

Face

Color layers

Grace Mandala

Mandala stencil and
stencil symbols

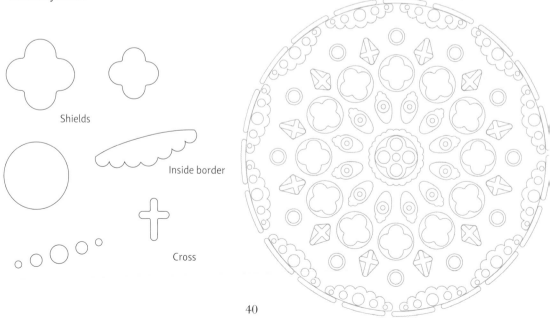

Shields

Inside border

Cross

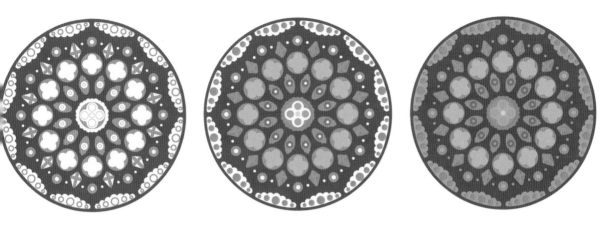

Color layers

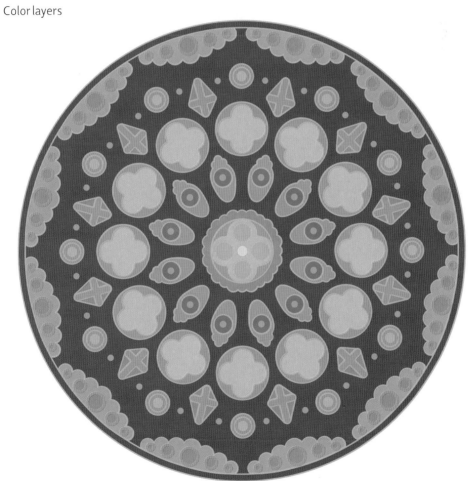

The four mandalas on pages 42–45 have each been created by combining the symbols from the six stencils.

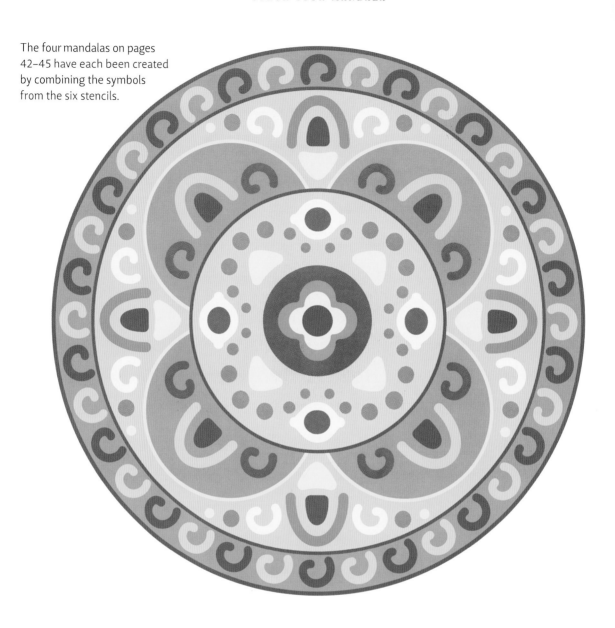

MANDALA SYMBOLS

Mandalas can have a multitude of symbols, depending on their cultural tradition. Here are a number of common symbols and their meaning in traditional mandala designs.

Circle The universe; wholeness

Circle with a central point The universe with its seed of creation

Circle containing a square Reconciling material and spiritual dimensions

Wheel Sacred circle with the four elements and four directions

Wheel of Life The processes of daily life

Cross Transfiguration

Square Earth, solidity

Egg Origin of the world

Upward-pointing triangle Masculinity

Downward-pointing triangle Femininity

Infinity Inherent balance, eternity

Spiral Evolution, growth

River Flow

Eye Perception, vision

Phoenix

Snake

Dancing

Moon Inspiration, intuition

Star, six-pointed Celestial attributes

Virgin Self-sufficient feminine power

Dove Peace

Owl Wisdom

Eagle Power

Lion Courage

Phoenix Rebirth

Butterfly Transformation

Snake Circle of life; potential energy

Unicorn Potential healing

Arrow Rays of the sun, search for knowledge, swiftness

Totem Animal spirits

Dancing figures Joy

Tree Life, roots, continuity

Maze Journey

Lotus Transformation

Rose Heart

Peacock feather Exhibition, knowing eye

Aum Sacred Sanskrit syllable; sound of the universe

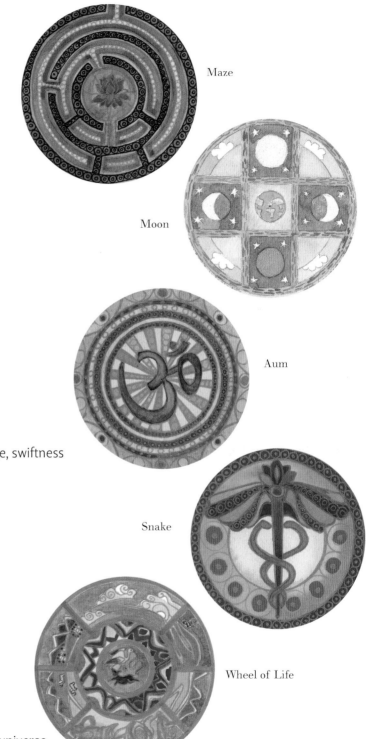

Maze

Moon

Aum

Snake

Wheel of Life

GAZING UPON MANDALAS

Contemplating a mandala acts upon you in a profound way; whether you ask for this experience or not, it will happen.

Just as the content of the mandala emerges in the process of drawing or creating it, so contemplating upon it acts upon you in a profound way—regardless of whether you formulate a specific intention when you sit down to look at it. Setting an intention can help you to focus on your personal journey, but Carl Jung believed that mandalas could have an almost magical power to act in a healing way upon your psyche. He suggested the process as an opportunity to reconcile internal conflicts and advocated mandala-making to facilitate integration. A function of creating a mandala is to bring order out of internal chaos.

.

FOCUSING ON YOUR MANDALA

Focus on your mandala in all its detail. Take in the beauty of the individual designs, allowing your eye to wander over its patterns and colors, becoming absorbed in the interplay of harmony or dissonance. Let the intricacies, patterns, and interplay of the different colors and other elements of the mandala draw you into it. Looking is not about judging your artistic efforts or analyzing the symbolism of the mandala, but allowing yourself to respond to what you have created and find a unique resonance for you... let thoughts or feelings arise naturally—or no thought at all.

A HEALING INFLUENCE

Jung believed that mandalas possess a "magical significance that you are not necessarily aware of by virtue of the potency of their symbolical content. This is what offers a healing influence to your unconscious mind. As circles are universally associated with meditation, healing, and prayer, you can work with your mandala in these ways. Enjoy

METHODS OF CONTEMPLATION

Lead us from untruth to truth
Lead us from darkness to light
Lead us from death to immortality
Aum, let there be peace!
— Vedic chant

According to the singer Chloe Goodchild, meditation comes in different forms: it can come through the naked voice, the liberated body, the penetrating vision, the empty mind, the loving heart, or the ecstatic embrace—a particularly tantric means of transformation.

The mandalas in this book present inspiration for meditation in a visual form. We all respond in different ways to visual stimuli and have our own styles of processing information, and these individual preferences can be incorporated into the mandala-making and meditations. For some of us the kinaesthetic sense—the awareness of our body's position and movement—is especially strong, so you may find that free movement liberates your creative mind. For most people sensory experience is important, so if touch, sound, smell, or taste is evocative for you, you may wish to incorporate it in your mandala-making

and your meditation. That is why some people use humming, incense, or essential oils to facilitate altered brain states.

WHAT DOES MEDITATION INVOLVE?

Meditation refers to an altered state of consciousness. This can be described in a host of ways, but often as a mental quality or an emotional experience. Words used to describe states of meditation include awareness, clarity, centeredness, equanimity, calmness, fullness, love, compassion, connectedness, bliss, and light... Practicing meditation often brings profound changes within weeks—you feel calmer, centered, patient, and less anxious. You awake refreshed. Your concentration improves and you feel happier and more confident. As you become calmer, you become more focused, and more in touch with your intuition and creative self.

50

WAYS TO ACCESS A MEDITATIVE STATE

The traditional method used by Buddhists is visualization. Summon up a visual scenario that feels revelant to you in your mind's eye, and once you feel you are really there, let the scene unfold. See where the unfolding scenario takes you.

You may follow a meditation you know from a class or a book, or impose your own narrative. You can do this by recording a meditation so you can follow the sound of your own voice. It's important to speak slowly in order to allow yourself space to think during playback.

Consider using mandala meditations with a friend or partner, or even a small group. Some people focus better in a group setting, and the relationship with others serves to intensify or to reflect changes within.

Take a word or a theme, read the meditation, or perhaps a poem, and then reflect on it. Examine its personal relevance and meaning, and freely associate on the theme.

Use a mantra—constantly repeat a phrase or a single word, such as "compassion." Repeating the mantra pulls your awareness back to the theme you are working on.

Recall a situation that has evoked particular feelings. Once you have summoned up the emotions, they can be transformed into positive feelings and directed toward other beings, projecting positive emotions toward different groups of people. The feelings are projected out universally, to everyone, regardless of your relationship with them.

AWARENESS

The Zen Buddhist Thich Nhat Hanh describes emptiness as full of everything and empty of nothing. Working with mandalas helps cultivate an awareness of this dual nature of reality, which consists of both form and emptiness.

SYMBOLS

The shield The detailed work on this mandala, inspired by a Celtic shield, draws your eye into its proliferating circles and flowing lines. Focusing on this detail will help you develop your ability to concentrate, thereby improving your awareness. Awareness is, in a way, "mindlessness." Mindlessness is the intelligence that is present when your mind stops thinking—intelligence that arises spontaneously. Being totally absorbed in the task at hand will allow your natural awareness to emerge. If engaging totally with the present proves difficult, try altering your focus slightly. While you concentrate on being fully aware of whatever is going on, also observe your own reactions, however they arise. As the Buddha said, "How can one ever know anything if they are too busy thinking?" Give yourself fully to whatever you are doing right now!

Enhancing your awareness is all about noticing the detail and being in the moment.

52

SHRI YANTRA FOR DIVINE LOVE

*Love is the essence of God in every mystical tradition.
In Sufism, poets used the metaphor of lovers to describe the
longing for union with God.*

SYMBOLS

Upward triangles represent the male; downward-pointing triangles symbolize the female. Feminine energy is also shown as red, and masculine energy is white. Their integration of male and female is shown by the mixed red and white areas. You can work with other colors to represent this dynamic relationship, such as the hues of the earth and sky in ancient Egyptian art, the sky is masculine, the father, and the earth, feminine); or, simply choose a palette that for you represents love. The central triangular motif defines this design as the Shri, or "Great" Yantra (yantra is derived from Sanskrit words meaning control and liberation).

Lotus petals reveal purity and creation. The yoni (shown with the lotus petals) symbolizes female sexual power and ultimate creation.

The circle has many associations—perfection, eternity, protection. It represents the mandala itself.

Work with the colors that symbolize love for you, or draw upon other traditions, such as earth and sky colors seen in Egyptian art.

COMPASSION

This mandala depicts Tara, a goddess believed to have been formed from tears of compassion, regarded by many tantric Buddhists as the savior of all. Her whole body is made of light and she holds a lotus flower, symbol of regeneration.

SYMBOLS

Tara is an enlightened being whose image came into Buddhism through early Hindu pantheons of goddesses. The goddess Tara is used for Tantric meditation for the development of spiritual qualities. She comes in many colors, usually green or white; green for enlightenment, or white for compassion, healing, and serenity. Green Tara is depicted as an icon in a posture of ease as well as readiness for action. Her left hand gestures for the granting of sanctuary, while her right grants boons.

The lotus flower held by the goddess is a symbol of both purity and power.

The moon disk sits behind the head of Tara, focusing the mind upon her image. A full moon disk crowns each of the lotuses, symbolizing the realization of spiritual potential. The moon, associated with the feminine, features in many traditional mandalas.

Tara is usually white or green, but may be red, for energy; black, for power; yellow, for prosperity; or blue, for working with anger.

FORGIVENESS

Lack of forgiveness is one of the most corrosive of negative emotions. Forgiveness is the key to inner peace because it transforms your attitude from fear and blame into love and acceptance. It is not a sign of weakness, but of strength.

SYMBOLS

Open hands Lack of forgiveness can be a barrier to feeling connected with others. Unfortunately, we end up punishing ourselves on top of the trauma we feel that we have already experienced at the hands of others. Open hands symbolize a readiness to surrender and accept happiness rather than withdraw into continued resentment.

Feathers Feathers are often acknowledged as a sign from spirit, and for some, a sign of angelic presence. If you feel stuck, you can ask for grace to free up a situation, and to free yourself from your unhelpful reactions. In circumstances in which you find it difficult to let go, call upon a higher power to help you.

Lotus flowers in this mandala represent purity of intention, and the empowerment that forgiveness can bring you.

Working with a palette of pale colors creates a landscape of lightness and freedom from resentment. What may be needed is to let go, allowing the resentment to float off like a feather.

THE WHEEL OF LIFE

The Wheel of Life, or Wheel of Becoming, known as the Bhavachakra, is a Buddhist representation of samsara, the cycle of birth, life, and death, from which we may liberate ourselves through enlightenment.

SYMBOLS

The Wheel of Life represents daily life; the cycle of birth, life, and death, but also reincarnation. In the Western Tarot, the wheel of life is more about fortune, or destiny, symbolizing the workings of fate.

The elements The four classical elements of Earth (the green and brown mountains within the wheel), Water (the river on the plain), Fire, and Air are contained with the largest ring of the mandala, indicating the four fundamental qualities of existence.

Yama, God of Death holds the wheel to remind us that all life is transient, like a memento mori.

Cockerel, snake, and pig, in the center of the mandala, represent the three emotions that Buddhists believe need to be transformed to create a more integrated personality. The cockerel stands for lust; the snake, aggression; and the pig, ignorance.

This mandala is calm at its center—all the bustle and profusion of life turns around it. Experiment with calm central colors to contain the chaos of life.

WISDOM

Wisdom is not merely knowledge, but a deeper level of knowing than the intellectual mind can attain. It is the primordial intelligence of life. You are more likely to gain access to this dimension through stillness. Cultivate the habit of being still.

SYMBOLS

The fish In this mandala, the fish swimming toward the center point and outward to the perimeter expresses the mind's incessant flow. Buddhists believe that the fundamental nature of the mind is stillness. If you allow yourself to become calm and still, your mind will automatically settle down, creating a sense of inner peace and contentment, and your natural wisdom can flourish. Like a fish who allows the water to carry it to whatever it needs, you can allow your mind to flow, trusting that what you need will come to you.

The endless pathway This variation on the classic endless knot presents a path that has no beginning or end. Following this path helps calm the mind and open up to innate wisdom. In Buddhism, the endless knot expresses the infinite wisdom of Buddha.

Paint the pathway in the design a little at a time as a meditative exercise on opening up to wisdom.

LOVE

Love brings out the best in everyone and creates more positive energy in the world. Cultivate a loving heart, a loving partnership, and a loving home for your family to thrive in. By giving more love, you are more able to receive it.

SYMBOLS

Yab-yum Yab-yum is the Tantric term for lovers in an embrace, who sit together in ecstatic union inside the central lotus of this mandala. Together they symbolize the marriage of insight and compassion. Within a relationship, this becomes a willingness to relate deeply and to keep your heart open, regardless of whether others behave lovingly toward you. It involves letting go of expectations and control, and simply allowing others to be themselves.

Fire The energy of the base chakra (see page 23) is represented by fire. Just as sacrificial fires are used to reduce substances to their essence, so contemplating the symbol of fire can purify desire and transform raw passion into love and commitment.

Stars The stars around the couple in the lotus flower symbolize guidance and spirituality.

In chakra healing (see page 23), green is associated with the heart chakra, but work with any colors that resonate with love.

LOOKING

Gazing at something is considered in the East to be an active mode of engagement. That is why beauty is so important, as the quality of what you look at is thought to affect your own energy field. The eye is the window to the soul, associated with intuition.

SYMBOLS

The third eye links with the third-eye chakra. It is located between the brows (see the face, center). In ancient healing systems, such as that developed by Hindus, seven principle chakras, or energy centers, are mapped to the human spine, each related to different qualities of energy: the base chakra at the base of the spine, the sacral chakra below the navel, the solar plexus beneath the ribcage, the heart chakra at the heart, and the throat, brow, and crown chakras, as shown on page 23). The third-eye chakra is considered the seat of the teacher within you—what we would term your inner knowledge. It is regarded as the gateway to inner realms and higher consciousness, so is associated with intuition or light. Activating your third eye is believed to open you up to intuition, clairvoyance, and imagination.

Gaze upon the Looking mandala, and then color in your own to spark intuition and imagination.

67

PERSONAL POWER

The center of personal power is in the hara, just below the navel. Meditators and martial arts practitioners develop a powerful hara. Working with this mandala helps generate the energy you need to take your unique place in the world.

SYMBOLS

Three trees Three is a dynamic number of creatio The trio of trees symbolize growth, wellbeing, an strength. Rooted deep in the ground, they act as reminder that inside you are endless reserves energy and personal power.

Celtic knot The Celtic knot in this manda symbolizes a sure framework for the emergin sense of self. When you have inner certainty abo the way you choose to live your life, you gain pow and confidence. Any recognition from others is bonus, not the reason for seeking empowerme Your motivation is more to do with activating yo hara, which is like a solar panel or battery that c be charged up. Anything that promotes physic wellbeing will build up your store of energy.

A palette of vibrant colors creates energy, helping you engage w the theme of empowerment through the mandala.

DANCE

Like the dancing Shiva in this mandala, your body is a temple, dedicated to the life force. Through it, divine energy flows. Let your body express this—dance manifests the dynamic principle of being. Explore it with this mandala, coloring to music if you wish.

SYMBOLS

Shiva, Lord of the Dance Devotees of the Hindu god Shiva say that the world was danced into existence. The familiar image of him as the Cosmic Dancer or Lord of the Dance, performing this dance among the flames of the universe, represents the primal creative force. In dance you allow your life force to enliven your body, and encourage your body to express your connection with life. Your dance can be joyful and passionate, or tentative and exploratory. It can be all things depending on where your body and your mood take you.

Shiva's drum, snake, crescent moon, and bowl As an aesetic, Shiva carries his bowl for alms. He has overcome earthly passions (snake), transforming them into spiritual wisdom (moon), and holds a drum which beats out the sound of creation.

Listening to music can help you visualize colors for your mandala; its quality may guide you to muted or vibrant colors.

CONNECTING WITH THE COSMOS

This mandala emphasizes the multiple connections that weave through all life forms. Use the meditation to feel your connection with the cosmos as its energy flows through you and the earth receives your own.

SYMBOLS

The dot In mandalas, the central point or dot often represents the universe, reminding us that reality is beyond space and time. A dot is like a seed which contains the potential of infinite energy in the apparent nothingness of the universe. Each of us may be as insignificant as a dot of energy in the vastness of the universe, yet we all have our unique place within it. The jade disk of the Chinese has a hole in the center representing the universe—some traditional mandalas use one of the sacred names of god to represent this primal source.

Fish represent flow in this mandala, expressing the flow of life connecting us to the source, the universe.

The sea The sea is a vast world of emotions and subjective experience. A symbol of the unconscious, it is a realm teeming with life that we all swim in, but may also threaten to overwhelm us with its intensity.

The Cosmos mandala invites primal, earthy colors, and those that ring with life and energy.

HEALING

Symptoms are a sign of "dis-ease" or imbalance in the body or psyche. Whatever symptoms you wish to explore, whether pain or unresolved emotional issues, bring them to mind and focus on them as you color your mandala. Healing is an infinite resource that anyone can tap into.

SYMBOLS

The lotus flower at the base chakra indicates the source of the energy that is believed to stream through the chakra system (see page 23). Located at the level of the genitals at the base of the spine, this energy center is related to our sense of security in the world. In Tantra tradition, kundalini, the vital life force, is visualized as a snake coiled at the base chakra. The snake is activated according to our emotional, physical, and spiritual experience, and its level of vitality is an indicator of our wellbeing.

Channel/water The flow of energy above the crown of the meditating figure is depicted as water. This is the channel through which we are all connected with the Divine, with the universe, the source of healing and light. Use this channel to visualize light or color pouring into your pain body.

The colors associated with the chakra healing system are red, orange, yellow, green, blue, and indigo, and violet or white.

WATER

Water is associated with cleansing, the flow of our emotions and the unconscious. We can swim with the currents of our inner life without needing to identify with particular emotions, which are forever changing, like all of life.

SYMBOLS

Fish In this mandala, the fish represents the flow of emotional currents, which circulate naturally. Tail to tail, they may also indicate stuck emotions—going round in circles—but also the potential for accepting the current and the ebb and flow of life.

Seaweed Seaweed growing in the ocean symbolizes our existence and validity as emotional beings.

Water/ocean The ocean symbolizes emotions. Emotions are part of your inner life, and many people feel they have responses to life that are as deep as the ocean. Rather like a surfer on the crest of a wave, the trick is to enjoy the thrill of feeling emotions, without getting sucked under through identifying with a particular emotion. Whether it is pride or envy, anger or sadness, malice or martyrdom, none of them defines our true nature. All these emotions are transient, and we can flow through them.

As you color your mandala, you may want to sit where you can hear the gentle sound of running water for inspiration.

GRATITUDE

This mandala celebrates being alive. There are so many good aspects to your life; try to give thanks for them every day. Start by making a list, and then focus on appreciating each and every gift.

SYMBOLS

The cosmos symbolizes an awareness of the world above us; when we express gratitude, we often look to the sky as an acknowledgement of the Divine. The sky also invokes mindful awareness.

Hearts and hands express giving and receiving, in which the ultimate gift is the exchange of love.

The phases of the moon indicate the cyclic nature of thankfulness; the expression of gratitude feeds positive relationships over time. The darker moon phases show that it may be difficult to feel thankful when you feel in shadow, but to do so helps release negative feelings and brings you back into balance.

Water connects with the moon phases as the moon controls the tides. From water, we move through the mandala to the earth nurtured by it, then back to the heavens and central moons and tiny guiding stars.

Some of the items or people on your gratitude list could become symbols to add into your Gratitude mandala.

DEITY PRACTICE

This is a lovely mandala in which you can use the image of a deity figure such as a god, an angel, or a saintly figure to evoke divine qualities, which you can then generate in yourself. We are all sacred manifestations of the Divine.

SYMBOLS

The angel represents compassion and protection. You may like to include your idea of the divine in your mandala as a person or object that is symbolic of the qualities you wish to cultivate. Traditional symbols or icons include a snake, a golden egg, the Buddha, and the Virgin Mary.

The heart Here, the heart is cracked and held by the angel, a beneficient figure who protects and heals it, just as visualizing a deity can be a useful practice to release hurt and ask for help. Surrendering problems releases energy and encourages self-healing and strength, thus overcoming a sense of helplessness.

Root and seed The roots and seeds express how this kind of deity practice encourages personal growth. The roots show security and trust, while the seeds symbolize potential knowledge and growth.

A deity depicted with seeds and roots symbolize asking for guidance from a deity to bring personal growth.

BEING OF SERVICE

Learning to put someone else's needs before your own can be a real lesson in spiritual growth. That's why your children are often your best teachers—their demands won't allow you to disengage with life or focus too much on your problems.

SYMBOLS

The heart In classical times the heart was considered the seat of the mind, the emotions, or the soul. Today, we associate it with ideal love. In this mandala, the heart symbolizes love in the context of service to others. It is positioned near the top of the mandala to indicate the ideal of service as putting others' needs above your own because you love them. Each act of giving or caring affirms our interdependence. Rather than focusing on what you imagine you need, focus on what you have to offer others.

The sun/petals represent solar power, the sun, and its association with growth and healing.

Trees Trees support the sun/petals and heart motif, symbolizing emotional strength available to others. Branch to branch, they suggest the gathering of strength as part of a community.

You may want to create this mandala for someone who is ill, as a way to tune in to their needs.

CHAKRA

Chakra techniques teach us how to purify and invigorate Kundalini, the energy center at the bottom of the spine, at the base chakra. The purpose of raising Kundalini energy is enlightenment, when you become fully integrated.

SYMBOLS

The seven chakras There are seven principle chakra points along the spine, and hundreds of minor ones, making a network of subtle energy channels. Energizing the chakras through movement, breathing, and meditation is used to help the kundalini on its journey from the base of the spine and up toward the crown of the head.

The shri yantra of divine love (see page 54) at the seventh chakra (the crown) symbolizes divine love. The seventh chakra is the gateway to the divine.

The cosmic dancer represents the spiritual focus of the meditating figure. A chakra meditation involves breathing deeply, imagining the energy gathered by the breath moving through each chakra in turn, visualizing each chakra's associated color: red, then orange, yellow, green, blue, indigo, and violet or white.

Doing the simple chakra meditation can help connect you with the key colors you want to work with when coloring your mandala.

MASCULINITY

In tantric rituals, masculinity is represented by the vajra, a Sanskrit word meaning thunderbolt or diamond. Symbolized by a diamond sceptre, the vajra, or Tibetan dorje, stands for potency, action, incisiveness, power, and indestructibility.

SYMBOLS

The vajra is a Tibetan Buddhist symbol which represents focus and clarity. In Western culture, the vajra could be replaced by the scepter, symbol of authority possessed by kings and priests. In legend it was wielded by Indra, who in Vedic times was the supreme ruler of the Hindu gods, the god of war and storms, and the greatest of all warriors. Among the classic masculine archetypes of the king, the warrior, and the magician-healer, the true warrior is considered the one able to sum up a situation and take direct action to bring positive change. Although powerful, he acts wisely and takes care not to harm others. Aggression, the typical attribute of immature masculinity, is repulsive to the warrior. The most challenging task for the warrior is to look unflinchingly at his attitudes, expose their limitations, and step beyond them to step forward and wield a power symbol—whether vajra or sceptre.

The vajra is associated with indestructibility, and its mandala may encourage sharp, defined color.

FEMININITY

Femininity is divine, and manifests the qualities of the Goddess, or the Great Mother. In the East, the feminine is passionate, earthy, powerful, expressive, open, giving, caring, sharing. She is all-powerful, all-seeing, and compassionate.

SYMBOLS

Shakti The Hindu goddess Shakti is associated with dynamic energy. While masculinity is associated with consciousness, both are needed to manifest all of life, in a holistic universe. Eastern traditions have always regarded women as sexually dynamic, and initiators of men. This role was once enshrined in temple dancers. In Greek and Roman mythology, the goddess Artemis/Diana, the huntress, represented the vital go-getting aspect of women. Shakti holds four symbols of her dominion over aspects of life: the snake, drum, trident, and vase.

Rose petals The eight rose petals surrounding Shakti have within them concentric shapes of dark coral and red—some are almost heart-shaped—with a pink central motif symbolizing the yoni, or female genitalia. In Tantra, the color red symbolizes feminine energy, whereas white symbolizes the masculine.

Dynamic colors are often associated with Shakti, a goddess and metaphor for femininity.

SEXUALITY

Tantric practitioners have long known that sex can be a gateway to ecstatic experience, extending your awareness of bliss. Deepening the sexual energy between you and your beloved means connecting to the primal erotic energy of creation.

SYMBOLS

Shakti and Shiva In Tantric tradition, the marriage of man and woman is represented by the image of the god and goddess in sexual union. The fruits of their divine connection rain down upon the world as nectar. Cultivating this sacred model in your lovemaking is believed to align you with the perfect god and goddess. An advanced practice in Tantric meditation is to visualize Shakti and Shiva making love above the crown of your head. The golden nectar rains down into a winged chalice positioned where your third eye would be; thus you bathe yourself in ecstasy.

Petals/flames of red and green In this mandala, the petals/flames beneath Shakti and Shiva are red and green, symbolizing the red fire of sexuality and femininity, and the green of the heart chakra, which is a representation of love.

Experiment with different shades of reds and oranges, pinks and greens to evoke love and sexual passion.

CONCEPTION

According to tantric philosophy, conception occurs when the lovers' energy bodies are revitalized by the energy of sexual ecstasy. A vortex of swirling energy rises up through the crown of the head and attracts a soul that is already waiting to be reborn.

SYMBOLS

Lotus flowers, symbols of regeneration, are shown with flowing stems, linked almost umbilically to the curve of their circles. The four mandalas are mandalas in microcosm, and appear as human cells, which suggests, too, the mandala as a symbol of the microcosm as well as the universe. The four flowers are in full bloom, standing as a mature family around the growing seed.

The seed symbolizes the fertilized egg, the beginning of a baby. In Tantra, the ovum is fertilized in the consciousness of woman's bliss, which attracts the new life.

Water represents flow and connection between the four flower circles, surrounding the central image of the ripening seed. The essence of life, it will also nourish the seed, echoing the amniotic fluid.

The lotus, the key symbol, roots in the mud and sends up shoots that produce beautiful buds, as people also grow into beautiful flowers.

RELATIONSHIP

What is key to reciprocity and connection is allowing the "otherness" of the other. Let them be themselves without trying to change them. Express love through tenderness, caring, and compassion, and nurture the sexual side of your relationship.

he infinity symbol The two infinity symbols show e completeness and distinctness of each person in he relationship; the figure-eight shape of the infinity mbols represents two people's neverending love. he two symbols are interlocked, showing the close- ess of the pair in the relationship, and how a person an flow and merge into their partner while still taining their individual differentiation. In Western oteric tradition the infinity symbol is also known the lemniscate, and appears in the Tarot on cards ssociated with magic, creativity, energy, and rength —qualities implicit in a lasting relationship.

lue leaves Blue is associated with speaking the uth, and is linked with the throat center, the place communication. It is a reminder of the need for onesty and communication in a relationship.

loring the leaves red implies dynamism, and is also associated th the base chakra and the qualities of foundation and security.

95

SUCCESS

Success is about expressing your personality and vision of the world and following your own path in life. Few of us believe we are total successes or total failures. Learn to transform any doubts about yourself into a belief in your ultimate success.

SYMBOLS

The labyrinth is a key symbol in meditation practice and mandala design. The labyrinth, or maze, is a series of pathways leading to a center, and can be traversed both ways. By following the path and attaining the center, we become focused and attain acknowledged success. Yet all success is relative—one moment you are in demand, and the next you're out of favor. Fear of failure can make us sabotage the good things in life. We may also fear success, suspecting that fate will knock us down or others will no longer like us, through envy or competitiveness. But with an open, positive attitude, others will feel your empathy and respond receptively. Follow the labyrinth to the center and follow your passion. What you set your heart on is what you become. Allow yourself to take up more space in the world.

The labyrinth represents a journey leading to success and the expression of the self.

97

ABUNDANCE

The cornucopia is an ancient symbol of plenty: a horn of fruits, sea creatures, and shells, representing the abundance of nature. This mandala is about recognizing the abundance that is all around us and seeing that we are all part of the profusion of life.

SYMBOLS

The cornucopia or Horn of Plenty symbolizes abundance. Traditionally, it is associated with harvest and shows festive fruits and vegetables in a horn-shaped basket. As you color your mandala, concentrate on what it is that you need for your life to be more fulfilled. Invite the seeds of those qualities to come into your own life. Coloring the mandala in this way is akin to preparing the soil. When you have finished the mandala, let go and allow abundance to flow into you and all around you.

Hearts, coins, fruit Represent love, money, and health—the three things we wish for the most.

Water and air in this mandala symbolize the emotions and their release as a wish for abundance.

Incorporate your wishes into your Abundance mandala as a way to manifest possibilities.

SELF-ESTEEM

Your deeper nature is passionately engaged with life, even if you come across as shy and hesitant, but low self-esteem can hold you back and cause you to cut yourself off from others. Learn to value your own nature and make the most of your sensitivity.

SYMBOLS

The female form The circle of twelve vibrant women in this mandala reminds you that you are a shining being, as valued and worthy as any other. Each form is perfect in its vibrant energy, as is every female body. Self-doubt and insecurity can obscure your awareness of your personal power. Guilt, shame, self-hate, or fear can get in the way of engaging with life. Other signs of low self-esteem include settling for less because you think you don't deserve better, or simply being confused about what you want. Recognize your sensitivity as an asset, which keeps you in touch with your emotions and also with the vulnerabilities of others. As the female bodies taper to a point that pierces the central cell of the mandala, so self-esteem touches the center of our beings.

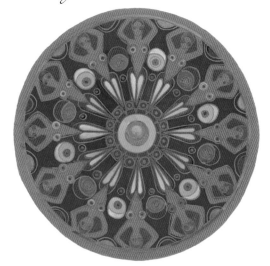

Incorporating the symbol of the body into a mandala affirms its artful beauty.

101

CHILDHOOD

To become more integrated and mature, many of us need to heal experiences from early childhood, turning them into lasting, character-building assets. This mandala focuses on the butterfly as a symbol of freedom and transformation.

SYMBOLS

The butterfly The butterfly symbolizes childhood innocence, growth, and freedom. When you gaze at this mandala or color it, let it bring back some happy experiences of childhood. Look at photographs of yourself as a child, to help you feel your way back into your childhood experiences. How would you describe your personal qualities then? What were your strengths and weaknesses? How were these aspects of you received? Did your parents appreciate you or did they try to make you change? Reflect on how you developed and worked on these qualities. You may find that the qualities that made life difficult as a child have helped you in your current life, that your own childhood has been your best teacher.

Let the Childhood mandala express the colors you loved as a child to create a sense of playfulness.

SUFFERING

Suffering offers the possibility of spiritual redemption, if you can find the resources inside yourself to transform your trials into growth. Spiritual practice involves asking yourself what lessons you need to learn for positive change.

SYMBOLS

The tree/cross The tree forming a central cross symbolizes the martyrdom that suffering can bring, but the evergrowing branches of the tree indicate growth, and a way forward out of the woods and back into the light. In very challenging or dark moments, opportunities for growth exist—indeed, without difficulty and challenges, it can be hard to sustain the effort needed to grow. Through this you can develop qualities you might not otherwise have, benefiting yourself and others.

Leaves The autumnal leaves symbolize the letting go of pain. Suffering can be the result of physical dysfunction or emotional pain. While we know that dealing with physical pain often demands that we surrender to it, many of us hold on to our emotional pain. By accepting suffering and fully experiencing it, we may heal ourselves.

Intense feelings can evoke intense colors. Working with this intensity can be a good way to express powerful feelings.

105

THE TREE OF LIFE

Trees shade us and nourish us. They are the lungs of the earth. With their immense fertility and longevity, they are universal sources of inspiration, and the Tree of Life has been a potent symbol in every ancient culture.

SYMBOLS

The Tree of Life symbolizes the uniting of heaven and earth; birth, maturity, death, and rebirth; or man's place in the universe. In some esoteric traditions the tree provides a "map of creation." Kabalah, the Jewish mystical system, describes the tree with ten sephirots, or expressions of the will of God: crown (divine will of creation), wisdom, understanding, kindness, severity, beauty, victory, foundation, and kinship. In Norse mythology the tree bestows insight and wisdom; the god Odin suspends himself from Yggdrasil, the World Tree, to gain the gift of prophecy.

The fruits of the Tree of Life symbolize fertility, wisdom, fruitfulness, and family. Man can be seen as one of the fruits of a tree. The tree and its fruits can also represent the collective and the community.

The Tree of Life is a spiritual and community symbol, an example of companionship and exchange.

EARTH

This mandala is for you if you live more in your head than your heart or body, as it could help you to feel grounded. Many of us feel ungrounded—we are driven by hectic lifestyles and are forced to communicate through depersonalizing modern technology.

SYMBOLS

Gaia Gaia is the Greek goddess of the earth who created the sky, hills, and sea. As an oracle of Delphi, Gaia was known as "the womb of the world." When we connect with her, it helps us feel grounded; inhabiting your body, and experiencing your body as being supported by nature. Use the mandala to feel even more physically and emotionally nourished by nature. If the weather is good, walk outside to be inspired by the sounds, smells, and other sensations of nature as stimuli for your artistry. Gaze at a plant or flower, or find a quiet space and visualize an image of nature, such as a wild stretch of coast or a sacred grove. Bring what you sense into your mandala, noting the colors and energy of your experience.

Exploring the Earth mandala is a way to feel more grounded in mind and body.

109

PAIN

Pain can feel like a tormenting demon that cuts right into you. Severe pain goes to your very essence. People who have learned pain management strategies say that ultimately you have to surrender to it, rather than trying to fight it.

SYMBOLS

The serpent and staff A staff and singular entwined serpent (the rod of Asclepius) and a winged staff with two serpents (the caduceus) have both been associated with healing over the centuries. In Greek mythology the staff and serpent were borne by the healer-god Asclepius, son of Apollo; the emblem symbolizes rejuvenation and support. The staff and serpent symbol is central, and overlays a sunlike disk, in this mandala representing the healing of pain. Together they suggest the experience of pain and its respite. Meditation may help with pain management—creating a focus that illuminates the gaps between bouts of pain can help calm anxiety. When anxiety is reduced, this can help break the cycle. When you color this mandala, consider the colors that express pain and meditate on those that express non-pain, or release.

For the Pain mandala, consider the balance of color to express pain and the gaps between pain.

FLOW

"Flow" is a state of heightened experience that athletes, artists, and musicians may have when they are completely absorbed in expressing their creativity authentically. Being authentic involves being true to your vision and doing whatever it is that needs to be expressed.

SYMBOLS

Fish In this mandala, the fish represents the unconscious self and the creative charge. Flow happens when our judging, conscious mind steps to the side and allows our innate creativity to be expressed. For some this creativity could be seen through playing a musical instrument; for others it could be through teaching, gardening, writing, singing, parenting, or meditating. It doesn't matter whether others see it as worthwhile—this is about what you want to express. The golden rule for entering your flow is to follow your heart's desire.

Endless knot This variation on the classical endless knot expresses the concept of creative flow, like the fish, and also suggests a pathway for our creative flow, which is channeled in a productive way.

The process of coloring and gazing upon mandalas helps strengthen your creative flow.

113

BOREDOM

Do you dare to taste your own experience and feel your power?
To be free and happy, you may have to sacrifice boredom, a sign
of disengagement with life. Work with this mandala to help
regain your inner dynamism.

SYMBOLS

Lizard In this mandala, the lizard or gecko symbolizes the self waiting to escape the enclosure of boredom. Yet the creature, like the mind and spirit, is fully animated and can leap out of the circularity of its thinking at any time. We often use boredom to cushion ourselves from painful emotions or feelings of emptiness. To replace the discomfort with more pleasant sensations, we become reliant on stimulants like sugar, chocolate, cigarettes, alcohol, drugs, or medications. Boredom indicates we have lost interest in the richness of life. The way through it is to let go of your tension and agitation, inhabit your life fully, and find your inner resources. Go inside yourself, because what you'll find there is intrinsically interesting. Let the lizard symbolize your boredom, transform him with color and detail, and create something of beauty and fascination.

Working with a repeat motif such as the lizard allows you to focus solely on color and creating vibrancy.

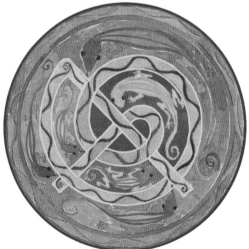

114

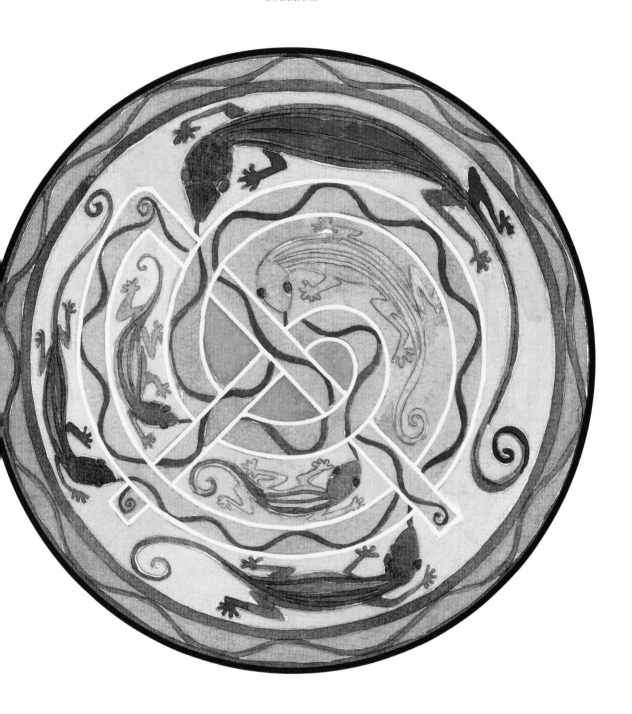

116

CREATIVITY

Your passport to creativity is passion—applying your energy to doing whatever moves you deeply. The closer you are to your own sources of inspiration, the more you will want to manifest that energy, and to share it with others.

arrot The parrot is the symbol of Kama, the Hindu od of passion and desire. By taking pride in what ou are passionate about, and expressing this assion, you stay connected to your creative source. our sources of inspiration provide a direct channel r creative energy. You can be creative in your style f living or you can give birth to ideas, projects, or ings of beauty or meaning. That includes your ildren! The most important aspect of creativity is njoyment—we are all born with whatever roduces the creativity, but it can be knocked out of s by social pressure to conform. You know the rocess that stimulates creativity, so you know what ou need to do to put yourself there. The parrot is so associated with talking and communication, so member that the creativity process always enefits from others' input.

hat inspires you? Your passion is the source of creativity, so look ound you for it and bring it into your mandala work.

117

PLANTING THE SEED

This mandala uses the garden as a metaphor for planting seeds in your life and then nurturing the plants. Be clear in your mind what result you are looking for—the kernel containing the potential of what you desire—as you will get what you invoke.

SYMBOLS

The seed Bean pods connect with roots and branches, symbolizing cosmic eggs, vessels of all life.

The beech and oak leaf The beech tree is associated with help, hope, and versatility. The oak is linked with reliability, endurance, and longevity. In Celtic mythology, the oak's roots grow deep into the Otherworld, a paradise where the gods and spirits reside, while its trunk lives in the physical world of mankind.

Earth colors As you color this mandala, focus on preparing the ground in your psyche. Imagine you are turning it over, feeding it with compost so that it is receptive to the seed you wish to plant. Visualize turning the earth with your paintbrush or pen, with its rich, dark colors and heavy, moist odors.

Focus on the image of a seed or pod before you begin your mandala. Experiment with rich earth pigments.

INVOCATION

Physicists can detect sound waves from the universe. To us, such vibrations may only be perceptible when we turn our attention away from the incessant noise of the world around. You can tune into this inner sound—the sound of creation—through reciting "Aum."

SYMBOLS

Aum The Sanskrit word Aum has often been used to attune the individual with this cosmic hum. Reciting a mantra with Aum focuses the mind on the inspirational energy of sound, filling you with power. Aum, which yogis believe is the primal sound of the universe, stands for the supreme reality. It represents what lies behind the past, present, and future. According to the Mandukya Upanishad:

A: is waking life and the mastery of the senses.

U: dream states in which you can access inner wisdom.

M: corresponds to silence, in which you still the mind to uncover your true nature.

You can use this mantra to attune yourself to the universe and the humming energy of creation.

You may choose to work with vibrant colors for the Aum mandala to mirror the humming of the universe implicit in the mantra. Feel free to chant while you work.

GRACE

Allow the sacred to touch your life, the way a shaft of light breaks through the clouds or filters through a stained-glass window. In Hinduism, the path of grace is from the universe, through the central energy channel of the body, the sushumna, which translates as "the most gracious."

SYMBOLS

Rainbow colors This mandala contains the seve[n] rainbow colors to symbolize light and sacrednes[s].

Three roses The three roses in the mandala's cente[r] echo the appellation "rose window," which gener- ally refers to the circular windows of intricate staine[d] glass that appear in many cathedrals throughou[t] Europe, and the inspiration for this mandala. Th[e] deep violet areas of the mandala represent wha[t] would have been built from stone and timber— material that divided areas of glass between window[s] were known as mullions.

Quatrefoils Within each of the 12 disks that form [a] prominent circle in this mandala is a quatrefoi[l]. Popular in Gothic architecture, this heraldic symbo[l] resembles a four-leafed clover.

The rainbow, which we see in many stained-glass windows, is see[n] as God's means of communication by certain pygmy peoples.

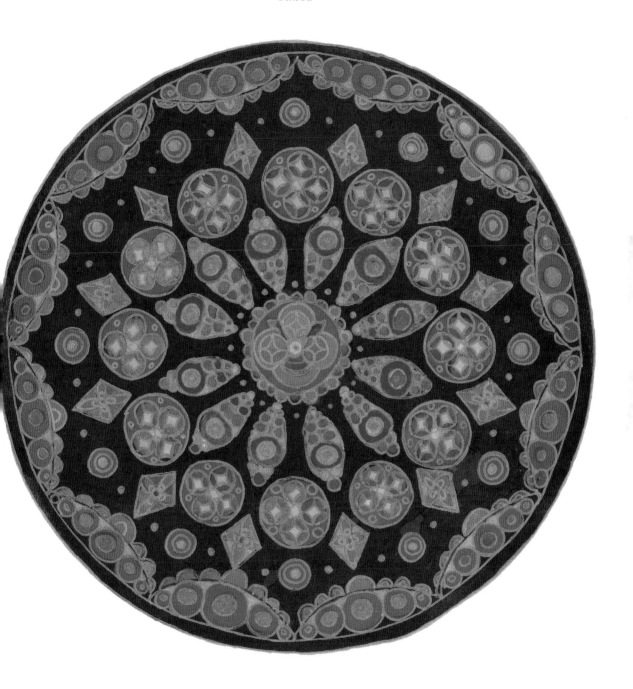

INTEGRATION

Carl Jung believed that our main task in life is to discover and fulfil our innate potential. The goal is to integrate all the disparate aspects of the self, even though it means tolerating the discomfort of increased self-knowledge.

SYMBOLS

The four segments of the Celtic knot Jung identified four basic psychological functions—thinking, feeling, sensing, and intuition. He said that because in most people only one or two of these predominate, it is good to develop the weaker functions. Also, because we all subconsciously attribute to others unacknowledged, negative aspects of ourselves, Jung said that what we most dislike about others may indicate what we need to work on and integrate within our own psyche. The four segments of the knot flow together, creating a symbol for integrating the four functions.

Winged creatures The tiny dragonfly, moths, and butterflies in this mandala symbolize the growth, energy, and freedom that comes with fulfilling our potential in life.

The Integration mandala has a four-segment knot that links together to symbolize wholeness.

IMPERMANENCE

Impermanence expresses the Buddhist notion that everything is constantly in flux, even planets and stars. Cultivating an acceptance of the transitory nature of our current situation helps us deal with change and loss.

SYMBOLS

The glyphs of the zodiac As symbols of change the zodiac glyphs are used by astrologers to char the fluctuating position of the planets in the cosmo and their relationship to one another.

The numbers 1 to 12 These twelve number describe the astrological houses that each zodia sign may fall into as part of reading a birth char However, in terms of symbolism, these numbers als express broader ideas of time and the transitiona nature of life. Because nothing lasts, our natura reaction is to grasp on to people or experiences, bu this can lead to emotional suffering. It is more health to learn to remain open to what comes into our live and accept the situation when it leaves. In this way we can become more adaptable and appreciative o the present moment.

The planets' transition through the cosmos symbolizes impermanence and the passing of time.

126

GRIEF

You can never really lose someone close, as the good things that came out of the relationship will always stay with you. The experience of satisfying closeness has nourished you and you have incorporated it into your psyche. This mandala features the spiral as a symbol of grief.

SYMBOLS

The maze or spiral The maze acts as a symbol of the cosmos, which expresses the turns, challenges, and search for happiness, or spiritual treasure at the center. Like the Integration mandala (see page 124), the four segments of the design relate to Jung's four psychological states of being: thinking, feeling, sensing, and intuition. Here, one segment is more heavily decorated to show how grief intensifies a particular state, which flows into our other sensibilities. The death of someone with whom you had a problematic relationship may be especially difficult, as you won't have had a chance to heal the split. In all instances, however, it is important that you first acknowledge the depth of your loss.

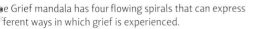

The Grief mandala has four flowing spirals that can express different ways in which grief is experienced.

KARMA

Karma refers to actions and their inevitable consequences, in an infinite chain of causation stretching back into the past and into the future. Because each moment in our lives is linked to the next, taking appropriate action requires awareness.

SYMBOLS

The alchemical snake The snake symbolizes the complete circle of life and, in this mandala, the impact of cause and effect. There is always a consequence to every action, whether spiritual, mental, or physical. If we speak in anger we will provoke an angry response. If we try to wound or manipulate, we will provoke a counter-attack. If we think unkind thoughts, we are likely to continue doing so. But if we generate loving thoughts, we are more likely to facilitate greater connection. We need to heal negative emotional habits in order to free ourselves of any destructive patterns.

The four elements on the outer areas of the shield are air (clouds), water, fire, and earth (grass and trees), which the ancients believed to be the fundamental building blocks of life: the cycle of nature mirrors the cycle of cause and effect, or karma.

Working on a Karma mandala encourages us to take responsibility for the impact of our attitudes and behavior.

PEACE

Peace is associated with restfulness, contentment, freedom, and fulfilment. It describes a relationship of respect, justice, and goodwill. For Mahatma Gandhi it was both a means and an end. Peace is a process, which we can create and recreate each day in myriad ways.

SYMBOLS

The peacock The peacock symbolizes compassion and peace. It is an ancient symbol, and in Hindu mythology was said to be a protector and destroyer of snakes, swallowing their poisonous venom without killing itself. The popular south Indian god Skanda, Lord Murugan, revered by both Hindus and Buddhists, was believed to have ridden on the back of a blue snake-killing peacock.

The triqueta The triqueta is a Celtic symbol of protection, of holding things safe. If you are at peace with yourself you might describe yourself as feeling balanced, serene, and calm. Inner peace is a state of mind, body, and soul, an inner quality. Even in the most unlikely circumstance, such as the midst of trauma or war, individuals have been able to maintain a state of inner peace.

Use this mandala to help you to preserve your own sense of peace whenever you feel in need of it.

DEATH

An essential part of preparing for death is a review of life, looking at past joys and sorrows and saying goodbye to each experience. Death will be the ultimate letting go and, according to all spiritual traditions, this requires some practice.

SYMBOLS

Kali-Shiva In Tantric iconography, the god Shiva meditates in the cremation ground, whitened with ashes, where the black goddess Kali rules supreme. Kali is the goddess of death, and her necklace of skulls reminds us of our ultimate destination. In this mandala, the images of Kali and Shiva are merged as one, as the deity's body is whitened with ash (Shiva) and adorned with the traditional skull necklace (Kali). This mandala offers an awareness of death, which may help you to live this day as if it were your last, letting go of distractions and the weight of accumulated sorrows.

The scythe and bowl Kali-Shiva's symbols show what must be taken and gathered from life.

The inverted triangles represent the feminine principle, or the goddess Shakti in Tantra.

Many traditions have developed visualizations on death, which may help our understanding of the process of letting go.

GUIDES

Think back to the people who have been important to you at different stages in life, and the varied ways they have guided you. Some mentors will have had a profound impact on you, perhaps even setting you in a different direction on your life journey.

SYMBOLS

The hand The helping hand is a symbol of guidance. It is reminiscent of the Khamsa, traditionally depicted as an eye in the palm of a hand. In Arabic and Jewish cultures, the Khamsa is a symbol of protection against the evil eye (in Jewish tradition it is known as the hand of Miriam). This mandala celebrates the power of guides, networks, and a helping hand; as you color it or gaze upon it, consider how each word of advice has helped sustain and nurture you. Some mentors were there with practical support, others with wise words, others leading by example. Let your mandala express their positive influence.

Inspirational fires In whatever form you have found it, true wisdom has been a light on your path. The flames symbolize this light and your search for it.

You may wish to dedicate your Guides mandala to a mentor, past, present, or future.

RITUAL

Many believe that creating rituals that affirm the sacred will encourage new, positive energies to manifest. Coloring a mandala is a ritual in itself; try any mandala in this book or create your own using the stencils. You can also add to the ritual atmosphere with meditation, perfume, and crystals.

SYMBOLS

Celtic knot In this mandala, the Celtic knot is a labyrinth for you to think about your own path to wholeness as part of a mandala ritual.

Rituals may incorporate: • lighting candles • working with crystals • working with essences, flowers, perfumes, essential oils • setting up altars • praying to realized beings or deities • sacrificing personal luxuries or possessions • chanting and dancing • meditating on mandalas.

Before you start, clear any clutter and air the room. Lay out any refreshments you'll need. Add your preferred sensory stimuli. Prop up your chosen mandala on a book stand, and begin.

Symmetrical designs can work well if you are approaching mandala-coloring as a ritual.

FURTHER READING

ach, Richard, *Illusions: The Adventures of a Reluctant Messiah* (Arrow, 2001)

ailey Cunningham, Lori, *Mandala: Journey to the Center* (DK Publishing, 2003)

orstein, Sylvia, *Pay Attention, for Goodness' Sake: Practicing the Perfections of the Heart–The Buddhist Path to Kindness* (Ballantine Books, 2002)

ampbell, Joseph, *The Hero with a Thousand Faces* (Princeton University Press, 1949)

hodron, Pema, *When Things Fall Apart: Heart Advice for Difficult Times* (Element Books, 2005)

hopra, Deepak, *The Path to Love: Spiritual Lessons for Creating the Love You Need* (Rider & Co., 1997)

alai Lama XIV, *Healing Anger: The Power of Patience from a Buddhist Perspective* (Snow Lion Publications, 1997)

oodchild, Chloe, *The Naked Voice* (Rider & Co., 1993)

uyser, Anneke, *Mandala Workbook* (New Age Books, 2006)

ng, Carl G., *Man and His Symbols* (Picador, 1978)

ornfield, Jack, *After the Ecstasy, the Laundry: How the Heart Grows Wise on the Spiritual Path* (Bantam Books, 2001)

adinsky, Daniel, *The Subject Tonight is Love: 60 Wild and Sweet Love Poems of Hafiz* (Pumpkin House, 1996)

evine, Stephen, *A Year to Live* (Thorsons, 1997)

orius, Cassandra, *Tantric Sex: Making Love Last* (Thorsons, 1999)

Preece, Rob, *The Alchemical Buddha: Introducing the Psychology of Buddhist Tantra* (Mudra Publications, 2000)

Reps, Paul, and Senzaki, Nyogen, *Zen Flesh, Zen Bones: A Collection of Zen and Pre-Zen Writings* (Turtle Publications, 1998)

Rinpoche, Sogyal, *The Tibetan Book of Living and Dying* (Rider & Co., 2002)

Spezzano, Chuck, *If It Hurts, It Isn't Love* (Hodder Mobius, 2001)

Vessantara, *The Heart: The Art of Meditation* (Windhorse Publications, 2006)

Williamson, Marianne, *A Return to Love: Reflections on the Principles of a Course in Miracles* (HarperCollins, 1992)

INDEX

Picture Credits